ELSIE
TIMES EIGHT

ELSIE
TIMES EIGHT

Story and Pictures by

NATALIE BABBITT

Michael di Capua Books

Hyperion Books for Children

This book is for
Margaret Billings Frattaroli,
my second grandchild

Elsie's fairy godmother loved her very much and came by once in a while to see how things were going.

One day Elsie's mama said, "Elsie has been such a good girl lately! You know, she didn't always do the things she should, before."

Elsie's fairy godmother meant well, but sometimes she
heard things wrong. "Elsie should be four?" she thought to
herself. "Dear me! Still, I guess I could do it."

So she waved her wand and changed the one Elsie into four Elsies.

This was a great surprise to Elsie and her mama and papa. It also surprised the cat.

As Elsie's fairy godmother was leaving, Papa ran after her and called, "No! WAIT!"

"Eight! That *is* a number," thought Elsie's fairy godmother. "Still, I guess I could do it."

So she waved her wand again and changed the four Elsies into eight Elsies.

And then she was gone.

What a time it was after that! For there was only one cat.
In fact, there was only one of everything. The Elsies fought
over all of it, and the noise was astonishing.

Papa had to bring in eight times as many vegetables from the garden, and Mama had to cook eight times as much for dinner. And there was only one chair for one Elsie.

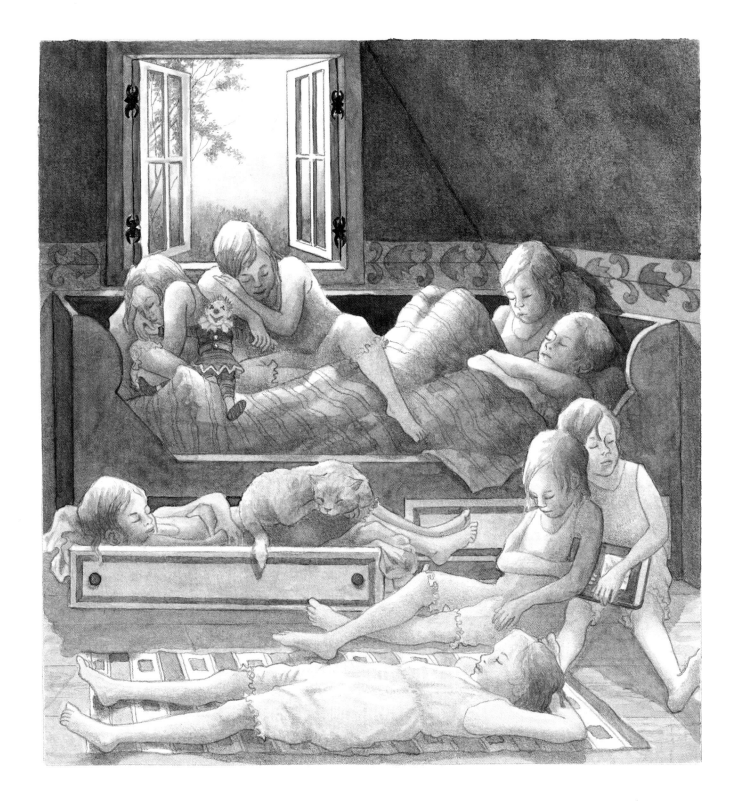

When it was time for bed, Papa and Mama couldn't keep track of which Elsies they had hugged and which they hadn't. And of course there was only one bed for one Elsie.

Day after day, the Elsies were noisy. It made the goats nervous, and annoyed the neighbors.

All the birds went somewhere else, and the cat was not pleased with it, either.

At last the Mayor came to the door. "You will have to do something about this rowdydow and racket," he said to Mama. "People are complaining."

But the Elsies paid no attention. They chased him away, and then they fought over his hat.

The Mayor sent a brave man with a message. It said, "Please return my hat. And you must move to another place at once, a place very far from here."

"It's that silly fairy godmother's fault," said Papa.

"There, there," said Mama. "She meant well. She'll set it all straight in a minute when we tell her."

But they didn't know where she was, so they had to do as they were told. When everything was packed, they gathered the goats, the cat, and the Elsies, and started off.

They walked and walked till they came to a new town far down the road, but nobody wanted them to stay there, for the Elsies were too noisy. So they had to keep on going.

Just then, however, a dog came by and barked at the goats. The cat was so alarmed that it ran to one of the Elsies and jumped into her arms.

"Aha!" said Papa. "The *cat* knows who's who." So Elsie's fairy godmother changed the eight Elsies back into the one holding the cat. For this was indeed the first Elsie. Cats never make mistakes.

"Next time," said Papa to Elsie's fairy godmother, "do try to hear things right. Goats you need more of, but one Elsie is enough. Even one cat ought to be plenty."

But Elsie's fairy godmother heard it wrong. *"Twenty?"* she said to herself. "Oh well, I guess I could do it." So before she flew away, she changed the one cat into twenty.

This was a great surprise to everyone, but not a bad surprise. Elsie liked it, and the cat was glad for the company.

And when they came home again, the neighbors were delighted. After all, twenty cats can manage quite a lot of mice.

So all the trouble was over.
Elsie's fairy godmother tried not to hear things
wrong again, and everyone lived quietly ever after.

But Elsie always knew which was the first cat.

(As for the mice, they had to pack up and move,
for mice do not like to be managed.)

DATE DUE

GAYLORD

PRINTED IN U.S.A.

Sound Trackers

1960s Pop

SOUND TRACKERS – 1960s POP
was produced by

David West Children's Books
7 Princeton Court - 55 Felsham Road
London SW15 1AZ

Picture research: Brooks Krikler Research

Published in the United States in 1999 by Peter Bedrick Books
A division of NTC/Contemporary Publishing Group, Inc.
4255 West Touhy Avenue
Lincolnwood (Chicago), Illinois 60646-1975 U.S.A.

Library of Congress Cataloging-in-Publication Data

Brunning, Bob.
    1960s pop/ Bob Brunning.
        p. cm. -- (Sound trackers)
    Summary: Highlights the influence of some of the important
performers on the popular music scene in the 1960s, including the
Beach Boys, the Beatles, Bob Dylan, Pink Floyd, the Rolling Stones,
Simon and Garfunkel, the Who, and Stevie Wonder.
    ISBN 0-87226-576-5 (hardcover)
    1. Popular music--1961-1970--History and criticism--Juvenile
literature. [1. Rock music. 2. Popular music.] I. Title.
II. Series.
ML3470.B78 1999
781.64'092'2--dc21
[b]   98-41697
                                                              CIP
                                                            AC MN

Printed and Bound in Italy

International Standard Book Number: 0-87226-576-5

99 00 01 02 03 10 9 8 7 6 5 4 3 2 1

SOUND TRACKERS

1960s Pop

HM 4205
15.95   AN 8/2000

Bob Brunning

PETER BEDRICK BOOKS
NEW YORK

CONTENTS

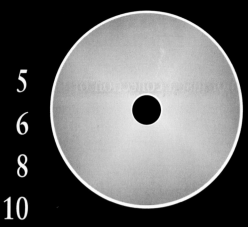

On these discs is a selection of the artists' recordings. Many of these albums are now available on CD. If they are not, many of the tracks from them can be found on compilation CDs.

These boxes give you extra information about the artists and their times.
Some contain anecdotes about the artists themselves or about the people who helped their careers or, occasionally, about those who exploited them.
Others provide historical facts about the music, lifestyles, fans, fads and fashions of the day.

The Beatles

INTRODUCTION

During the 1960s there was an explosion of talent on the popular music front in the UK and USA. Young people were enjoying a lot more freedom than their parents had ever experienced, and the aftermath of the late '50s rock 'n' roll influence encouraged many teenagers to start making their own music.

The author (far left) with Five's Company, before going on to join Fleetwood Mac and Savoy Brown.

With a modest outlay, four young people found that they could make a wonderful noise with a set of drums, a bass, a guitar and a microphone. There were certainly plenty of heroes to emulate. The Rolling Stones, the Beatles, the Who, the Shadows, the Kinks and many others achieved phenomenal success in the early '60s and proved that if you had some basic talent, however raw, there was a real chance that you could achieve pop stardom.

In the USA the Beach Boys, Jimi Hendrix, the Supremes and Little Stevie Wonder were among the most successful performers of the decade. Many of the performers and musicians were becoming confident enough to write their own songs, something quite new. During the '50s very few performers thought of doing this but relied instead on established songwriters to provide them with suitable material.

The '60s opened the door for huge numbers of young musicians to display their talent and we are still listening to the great music they produced today.

The BEACH BOYS

The name you choose when you embark on a career in the music business can be crucial. Would the Quarry Men (the Beatles), Harry Webb (Cliff Richard) and Robert Zimmerman (Bob Dylan) have become successful if they hadn't changed their names? In Los Angeles, California, three brothers formed a band. It was 1961. The band had various names until Brian, Dennis and Carl Wilson decided on one that reflected a passion shared by thousands of teenagers – surfing. Brought up next to California's golden beaches, the Wilsons understood the powerful thrill of challenging the biggest and the best waves. The band's new name? The Beach Boys.

"Surfin' Safari"
November '62
"Pet Sounds"
May '66
"Smiley Smile" November '67
"Sunflower" November '70

"The Very Best of the Beach Boys"
July '83
"Good Vibrations: Thirty Years
of the Beach Boys"
July '93

SURFING USA

The brothers invited their cousin, Mike Love, to join them. Al Jardine, a friend of Dennis, completed the Beach Boys' line-up.

The Wilson brothers had learned close harmony singing from their father, Murray. They put layers of harmony together with Chuck Berry-style guitar riffs and simple rhythms and the "surfin'" sound was born. They nervously recorded their first single, "Surfing," for the tiny Candix record label. The record entered the US Top 100. The huge Capitol record label soon spotted the potential of the Beach Boys. Several "surfin'" singles followed in quick succession.

Like many rock 'n' rollers before them, the Beach Boys recognized current teenage obsessions, the others being cars and girls. Brian Wilson's early lyrics dealt directly with these preoccupations.

The "Pet Sounds" album competed with the Beatles' "Sgt. Pepper."

UK AND THE WORLD

The Beach Boys had six singles and four albums in the US charts before they achieved success in the UK. But in June 1964 "I Get Around" made the UK Top 10. Many albums and singles followed that were hits all over the world. By the mid-'60s the Beach Boys were arguably the Beatles' main rivals.

But Brian Wilson hated performing and in 1965 gave it up to work in the studio. The band played on, performing and recording some of the finest music of the '60s.

THIRTY YEARS LATER

Over the next two decades, despite drug addiction and the need for years of therapy, Brian's musical genius and influence continued to shine. In 1998, 15 years after the death by drowning of his brother, Dennis, Carl died of cancer.

The innocence of the five beach bunnies singing about the pleasures of the sun, sea, surfing, girls, fast cars and rock 'n' roll has perhaps finally evaporated. But their legacy remains intact.

TEENAGE REBELLION

There was a reason for the Beach Boys' first success, which paralleled the appeal of bands like the Beatles, the Rolling Stones and the Who on the other side of the Atlantic.

A huge change was taking place in the USA. Young people were finding that they had power, socially and economically. They no longer had to mimic their parents, dress like them or listen to their kind of music.

On the West Coast the '60s surfing generation of teenagers lived for their dangerous sport, alarming their parents. The Beach Boys, representing this rebellious bunch, couldn't fail.

Murray Wilson (center) taught his sons to sing.

The line-up (from left to right) was Carl, Love, Jardine, Brian and Dennis.

7

The BEATLES

The Beatles are one of the best known groups in the history of popular music. They sold millions of records all over the world and the songwriting team of John Lennon and Paul McCartney produced dozens of classics which have been recorded by many musicians.

The Beatles with wax lookalikes in London's Madame Tussaud's.

"Please, Please Me"
March '63
"A Hard Day's Night" July '64
"Help" July '65
"Sgt. Pepper's Lonely Hearts Club Band"
July '67

"The Beatles 1962-1966"
April '73
"The Beatles 1967-1970"
April '73
"Live at the BBC"
December '94

EARLY DAYS

John, Paul, Ringo Starr and George Harrison sold out stadiums all over the world between 1962 and '66 but the original Beatles started out playing small clubs in the UK and Germany. Influenced by soul, rhythm and blues (R&B) and country and western (C&W) sounds from the USA, John and Paul joined forces in 1956 in a skiffle group named the Quarry Men. In 1958 they were joined by guitarist George Harrison and later by Stuart Sutcliffe (who stayed less than a year) on bass. In 1959 they were the Silver Beatles; in '60 Pete Best joined the retitled Beatles.

UNDER THREAT

In 1966 the Beatles went to play at the Budokan stadium in Tokyo. A powerful student faction considered the site sacred and threatened to kill them if they played there – so the Beatles had to stay locked in their hotel.

The Beatles' next concert was in Manila, where they inadvertently snubbed Imelda Marcos by declining an invitation to lunch. The whole entourage was attacked and barely escaped the country with their lives.

The Beatles made headlines all over the world by speaking passionately about their beliefs.

SUCCESS

In 1961 the Beatles were spotted by Brian Epstein in their native Liverpool. He secured them a record contract with the EMI record label and the Beatles started working with producer George Martin. In the same year Pete Best was replaced by Ringo Starr.

Seized upon by a generation of teenagers who craved a culture they could call their own, the Beatles quickly became the heroes of the young. Their first single, "Love Me Do," entered the charts in '62.

Their second single, "Please, Please Me," zoomed to the top – the first of 17 No. 1 hit records.

AMERICA BY STORM

The Beatles conquered the USA in early 1964, holding all five places at the top of the US charts. 1964 also saw the release of their film "A Hard Day's Night," with "Help" following in '65. The Beatles got tired of playing to hysterical audiences and stopped touring in 1966. They recorded many more albums and singles, including the innovative "Sergeant Pepper" in 1967, with its sitars, harpsichords and back-running tapes.

"Ready, Steady, Go" was the UK's weekly must-see pop music program on TV.

THE SPLIT

In 1968 the Beatles' manager, Brian Epstein, died and the group began to drift apart, with its members each developing solo careers. After less than a decade of the world hanging on their every note, the Beatles officially split up on December 31, 1970.

Tragically, in 1980, John Lennon was murdered in New York. However Paul McCartney, Ringo Starr and George Harrison are still working and producing music.

The influences of the Beatles' music can be found everywhere, even today.

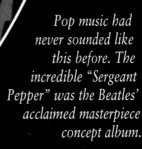

Pop music had never sounded like this before. The incredible "Sergeant Pepper" was the Beatles' acclaimed masterpiece concept album.

BOB DYLAN

Robert Allan Zimmerman was born on May 24, 1941, in Duluth, Minnesota. He graduated from the University of Minnesota and began to establish a reputation for himself as an accomplished singer, writer and guitar player around the student bars and clubs in Minneapolis. The poignant and moving songs that "protest" singer Woody Guthrie had written and recorded had a profound effect on Zimmerman, and he managed to travel to New York to meet his hero just before he died. During the short time left to Guthrie, the two became friends.

PROTEST SONGS

A fan of Welsh poet Dylan Thomas, Robert Allan Zimmerman became plain Bob Dylan. Dylan wanted to carry on the tradition of protest songs established by his folk heroes. There was no shortage of causes. During the

Police attend an anti-Vietnam war protest at the Pentagon in 1967.

1960s, the Civil Rights movement was growing in the USA, addressing the racism suffered by black citizens, and the deprivation of the poor. The threat posed to the Western world by nuclear weapons held by the USA and the then USSR was a source of real concern to many. Dylan wrote songs about it all.

"The Freewheelin' Bob Dylan" November '63
"The Times They Are A-Changing" June '64
"Bringing It All Back Home" May '65
"Highway 61 Revisited" Sept '65

"Blonde on Blonde" August '66
"John Wesley Harding" February '68
"Blood on the Tracks" February '75
"Bob Dylan at Budokan" May '79

RECORDING CONTRACT

The young Bob Dylan sang his heart out in the bars and coffeehouses of Greenwich Village in Manhattan. Word got around about his talent, and Dylan's astonishingly successful recording career commenced. Columbia Records executive John Hammond heard him playing.

He recognized Bob's talent and organized the recording of his first album. Costing less than $300 to record, "Bob Dylan" did not sell well. But Dylan's reputation as a protest singer was growing. He was confronting the issues which many Americans cared about.

In 1963, Dylan produced his first masterpiece. "The Freewheelin' Bob Dylan" album contained some classic songs, as did his '64 album, "The Times They Are A-Changing." Dylan's reputation as the foremost protest writer of the '60s was established.

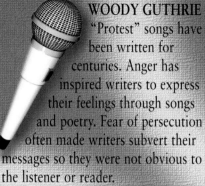

WOODY GUTHRIE

"Protest" songs have been written for centuries. Anger has inspired writers to express their feelings through songs and poetry. Fear of persecution often made writers subvert their messages so they were not obvious to the listener or reader.

In the 20th century writers have less to fear, and the '50s and '60s produced a crop of singers who used their songs to protest about what they saw as gross injustice.

During the '40s and '50s, the singer Woody Guthrie wrote and sang about the tens of thousands of Americans who had suffered appalling hardship during the Depression, a period when the US economy had crashed, creating mass unemployment. His work inspired many other singers.

WORLD FAME

In 1965 "Subterranean Homesick Blues" put Dylan in the US and UK charts for the first time. He performed all over the world. Some fans objected when he changed to an electric rhythm section using the versatile musicians The Band, but still his popularity was high.

TWO YEARS OFF

In 1966 a serious motorcycle accident nearly killed Dylan, and his recuperation took months. After a reclusive two years, Dylan returned to work and released over 20 albums during the next 30 years. And he plays on, as a member of the occasional Traveling Wilburys group as well as fronting his own band.

Guthrie in the cap that Dylan imitated.

Dylan performs with The Band, an experienced and talented team.

JIMI HENDRIX

Johnny Allen Hendrix was born on November 27, 1942, in Seattle, Washington. When he was three years old his father renamed him James Marshall Hendrix and 13 years later he bought him his first guitar. Left-handed, Hendrix reversed the strings and played it "upside down." Initially influenced by blues performers B.B. King, Muddy Waters, Chuck Berry and Robert Johnson, Hendrix soon developed his own style. After a short spell in the army, he moved to New York and played with many well-known rhythm and blues artists, including Little Richard, the Isley Brothers and Ike and Tina Turner. Hendrix's own bands were less successful.

SPOTTED

In 1966, Chas Chandler, the bass player with the well-known UK rhythm and blues (R&B) band the Animals, saw Hendrix in New York. Astounded by his persona and technique, Chandler acted. He brought Hendrix, now Jimi, to the UK. (On Hendrix's very first night in London, Chandler took him to see the band Cream, featuring a young guitarist called Eric Clapton. Hendrix joined them on stage that night.) Chandler organized a rhythm section for Hendrix. It comprised Noel Redding on bass and Mitch Mitchell on drums. He also arranged a recording contract with Polydor.

Hendrix played to 250,000 on the Isle of Wight.

FIRST SINGLE CHARTS

Hendrix's first single, "Hey Joe," was released in December 1966 and went to No. 6 in the UK charts. A label switch to Track followed, as did instant success. Hendrix was a creative songwriter and the hit singles came thick and fast, propelling Hendrix toward world-wide recognition. In 1967 Hendrix played the USA for the first time at the Monterey Pop Festival, burning his guitar at the end of his act to the stunned amazement of the audience.

NEW GUITAR SOUNDS

Hendrix was a great performer, playing his guitar behind his neck and with his teeth, but more than that he experimented with the electric guitar as no one had before, using the amplifier, phaser, wah wah and chorus pedals and slide to amazing effect. The Jimi Hendrix Experience became one of the world's most popular bands, but by 1969 cracks were appearing. Mitchell and Redding were fired for personal and business reasons. Hendrix replaced them and earned his place in rock history with his performance of "The Star Spangled Banner" at the most famous rock festival of all, Woodstock, in August '69.

JUST FOUR YEARS OF FAME

But tragedy was just around the corner. Hendrix played at the huge Isle of Wight Festival in August 1970. After a short European tour, he returned to London. Three years on the road, with all its temptations, caught up with Hendrix. He died on September 18, 1970, just 27 years old. He choked to death, very probably as a result of drug and alcohol abuse.

POP FESTIVALS

The emergence of huge outdoor rock music festivals in the '60s was linked to the development of modern PA (public address) systems. Before then no amplification set-up could deliver a clear sound to large open air arenas. The UK Windsor Jazz and Blues Festival with its state of the art Watkins PA system led the way in 1966. As PA systems grew in power so did the size of the audiences. The famous Woodstock Festival in 1969 attracted 500,000 people, although its 10,000 watt PA system barely coped.

You had to be an enthusiast to enjoy the experience. Awful food, inadequate toilet facilities, no shelter from the weather and the need for binoculars to see your favorite band were common problems at all the festivals!

Hendrix created a huge sensation at Woodstock.

Hendrix wasn't the first to play with his teeth.

The KINKS

In the early '60s many UK bands, such as the Rolling Stones, were being heavily influenced by the heady rhythm and blues music that was crossing the Atlantic. The Pretty Things, Manfred Mann, the Animals, the Yardbirds and the Beatles all featured rhythm and blues material in their recordings. North London group the Ramrods (later called the Ravers) were no exception, but were failing to make an impact. Then they met entrepreneur Larry Page, who remolded their image, bizarrely dressing them in hunting jackets, and changed their name to the Kinks. "There's nothing kinky about us though," said Ray Davies. "Kinky is such a fashionable word we knew people would remember it."

CARNABY STREET

One of the Kinks' most successful singles was "Dedicated Follower of Fashion." It entered the UK Top 10 in February 1966, capturing the mood of the new generation of young people who had money to spend in the boom '60s (a time of full employment) and wanted to follow the fashions of the day.

London's Carnaby Street and the King's Road, Chelsea, were arguably the center of fashion in the '60s. Posing, strutting and flaunting your new "gear" was all-important. Bands, of course, followed suit, and also tried to become innovators themselves.

A psychedelic print mini tent dress was high fashion in Carnaby Street in 1967.

HIT SINGLES

Led by Ray and his brother, Dave, the Kinks signed a record contract with the UK label Pye. Their first two unsuccessful singles were by other writers, but the brothers discovered that they could write their own, and with great success. In 1964 "You Really Got Me," with its memorable guitar riff, went straight to the top of the charts. The Davies brothers were talented songwriters and the hits followed. Over the next three years, they released a series of clever and amusing hit records which reflected their wry view of '60s England. Mostly written by Ray Davies, the lyrics of "Well Respected Man" (knocking the British class system), "Dedicated Follower of Fashion" (mocking '60s fashion fanatics), "Sunny Afternoon" (ruling class problems with the tax man) and "Waterloo Sunset" (even London can be picturesque), were direct and funny.

CONCEPT ALBUMS

A new idea was developing in the record industry in the 1960s – the "concept" album. A rock band would record a mini opera – not just a collection of unrelated songs, but an album which would carry a story, or devote itself to developing a theme. The Stones, the Beatles, the Who and many others produced concept albums. However, the Kinks' "The Kinks Are the Village Green Preservation Society" and "Arthur (or The Decline and Fall of the British Empire)" were ground-breaking albums of their type. "Village Green" was Davies' tribute to England and the quirks of the English character. "Arthur" (1969) was originally commissioned as a play for TV and its subject was an ordinary man reflecting on his life.

The Kinks' red hunting jacket phase did not last long.

FALLING OUT

Ray and Dave were growing apart by the late '60s and pursued solo careers in addition to their Kinks involvement. They had created a rift with the other band members, Mick Avory (drums) and Pete Quaife (bass), who left. With new musicians they carried on touring and recording to the end of the '80s – and had the honor of being inducted into the US Rock 'n' Roll Hall of Fame.

"The Kinks"
October '64
"The Kinks Are the Village Green Preservation Society"
July '68

"Arthur (or The Decline And Fall of the British Empire)" October '69
"The Ultimate Collection" September '89
"The Definitive Collection-The Kinks' Greatest Hits" September '93

15

PINK FLOYD

They started as the T-Set, became the Screaming Abdabs, then just the Abdabs. In 1965 George Waters, Rick Wright, Nick Mason and Roger Barrett took part of the name of a blues band called Pink Anderson and Floyd Council. They became The Pink Floyd Sound. They played rhythm and blues and gave powerful performances in London's clubs and pubs.

PSYCHEDELIC UNDERGROUND BAND

In 1966 they met Peter Jenner and Andrew King who became their managers. Their careers were about to take off. London was hosting a new "underground" music revolution and audiences were eager to hear bands who were daringly experimental.

Now simply Pink Floyd, the band stopped playing rhythm and blues (R&B) and concentrated on their own material – avant garde, experimental, psychedelic rock, written mainly by Roger, now Syd, Barrett. The band signed with the UK record label Columbia and released their first single "Arnold Layne," about a transvestite stealing women's underwear from clotheslines. It gave them their first Top 20 hit. The follow-up single, "See Emily Play," was even more successful and in August 1967 they released their first album, "The Piper at the Gates of Dawn," named from the children's book "The Wind in the Willows," by Kenneth Grahame.

"The Piper at the Gates of Dawn"
August '67
"A Saucerful of Secrets"
June '68
"Ummagumma"
November '69

"The Dark Side of the Moon"
March '73
"The Wall"
December '79
"Pulse"
June '95

BARRETT LEAVES

But soon there were problems within the band. Barrett's creativity was linked to his drug dependence. Eventually he couldn't function.

Dave Gilmour joined Pink Floyd and Barrett left. Barrett became extremely reclusive and never fully recovered from his drug addiction.

SUCCESS AND THE WALL

Pink Floyd became an "albums band" and one of the world's stadium-fillers. Their slow-moving songs could take as long as 20 minutes to develop and used unusual instruments and innovative sounds (such as the cash register ringing in "Money" and the clock sounds in "Time," both tracks on the "Dark Side of the Moon" album).

They used state of the art lighting and complex stereo and quadrophonic sound systems.

In 1973 "Dark Side of the Moon," with its theme of death and emotional breakdown, entered the UK and US charts and stayed there for years. Two more successful albums, "Wish You Were Here" and "Animals," followed and then, in 1979, "The Wall," almost certainly Pink Floyd's most famous work.

In the early '80s the band split. Happily its members continued to play and record the music loved by their millions of fans all over the world.

PSYCHEDELIC LIGHTS
The importance of lighting a stage to enhance drama has always been recognized but pop groups discovered its power only relatively recently.

Major bands like the Rolling Stones and the Beatles started their careers illuminated by a couple of 150-watt light bulbs. In the early '60s, musicians realized that the "look" of the band was almost as important as its sound.

Not the first to use psychedelic lighting, Pink Floyd started with the simple projection of swirling images produced by heating specially oiled slides. By the late '80s 20 trucks were needed to carry their lighting between concerts, and audiences were bowled over by the sheer spectacle.

Wright, Gilmour and Mason still used spectacular lighting in 1989.

The ROLLING STONES

In 1960, two students in their early 20s bumped into each other at a train station in South London. They remembered playing together at elementary school ten years before. But what caught Michael's eye was Keith's armful of obscure blues and rhythm and blues albums. It was a rare sight, and surprising to find someone else who was similarly passionate about his favorite music. And Keith was also a guitar player!

BLUES INCORPORATED

Michael invited Keith to join him and guitarist/bass player Dick Taylor in his amateur band, Little Boy Blue and the Blue Boys. All three often went to see the UK's first-ever rhythm and blues (R&B) band, Blues Incorporated, led by Alexis Korner at his London club. Sometimes the trio was invited to join Alexis on stage, a thrill for Mick and company. One night Brian Jones, a keen blues guitarist, was in the audience. He liked what he heard and joined the Blue Boys.

"The Rolling Stones"
April '64
"12 X 5"
November '64
"Big Hits (High Tide and Green Grass)"
November '66

"Their Satanic Majesties Request"
December '67
"Jump Back – The Best of the Rolling Stones 1971-1993"
November '93
"Stripped"
November '95

THE LINE-UP

Mick Jagger, Keith Richards and Jones formed the embryonic Rolling Stones. The band wasn't yet complete. Bass player Taylor and drummer Richard Chapman left. Bill Perks was recruited as the bass player because he owned a brand new amplifier and a van! Jagger and Richards occasionally used drummer Charlie Watts. They pressured him to leave his "day" job to join the Rolling Stones. His comment? "What's my dad going to say?" Bill Perks became Bill Wyman and the Rolling Stones were born.

IN THE BEGINNING

In 1962 the Stones piled into a van and drove from club to club. Andrew Loog Oldham spotted them and became their manager. He promoted them as scruffy, long-haired, dangerous-to-know bad boys – the opposite of the neat and suited Beatles. In 1962 parents did not want their daughters to marry a Rolling Stone!

By the end of 1963 the Stones had had two hit singles and their album, "The Rolling Stones," released in 1964, was massive. 31 UK Top 10 albums followed and 35 years later the Stones play on.

BRIAN JONES

By the late '60s, Brian Jones was beginning to cause concern to those who knew him. He was becoming increasingly dependent on drugs and alcohol. His health deteriorated and in 1969 the other members of the Stones had to dismiss him.

On July 3 in the same year, he was found drowned in the pool of his luxurious Sussex home. The Rolling Stones paid a tribute to Jones during a huge open air concert in London's Hyde Park a few days later.

Brian Jones' sad death was a reminder that, although the period known as the "Swinging '60s" was an exciting and liberating time for young people, there was a down side which should still serve as a warning.

The Stones play for Jones in Hyde Park in 1969.

NEVER ENDING

Self-styled "The Greatest Rock 'n' Roll Band in the World," in 1998 the Rolling Stones completed their Bridges to Babylon world tour, filling stadiums and thrilling millions of fans with their spectacular stage shows. Nobody seemed to care that three of the band members were grandfathers!

A custard pie fight launches the "Beggars Banquet" album.

19

SIMON and GARFUNKEL

In October 1964 Tom and Jerry finally decided to use their own names and recorded their first album together, "Wednesday Morning 3 AM," by Simon and Garfunkel. It included their version of the song "The Sound of Silence." The album was not a success. Simon went to Britain to try out the growing folk club circuit and Garfunkel went back to college. Under many different names Simon and Garfunkel had released 18 singles between 1958 and '62 but only one got into the US charts – at No. 49.

A HIT AT LAST

Producer Tom Wilson loved "The Sound of Silence." He remixed the song, adding a powerful rhythm section, and released it as a single. In December 1965 the record went straight to the top of the US charts and Paul Simon and Art Garfunkel got back together, quickly recording an album. It included an excellent song written by Simon at the Widnes railway station in the UK. (There is now a plaque on the station to commemorate the fact.) "Homeward Bound" was the follow-up single and was successful on both sides of the Atlantic. "I Am a Rock" came next, and went into the Top 10 in both the USA and the UK.

"Sounds of Silence"
March '66
"Parsley, Sage, Rosemary and Thyme"
October '66
"Bookends"
July '68

"Bridge Over Troubled Water"
February '70
"The Simon and Garfunkel Collection"
November '81
"The Concert in Central Park"
March '82

Their next successful album was "Parsley, Sage, Rosemary and Thyme," which included "Scarborough Fair" and the witty "59th Street Bridge Song." Naturally, Simon and Garfunkel capitalized on their chart success, touring all over the world between 1966 and '70.

Hoffman starred as "The Graduate." The film's soundtrack was memorable.

Their relationship on the road was occasionally uneasy, although they never resorted to the Everly Brothers' demands for separate hotels!

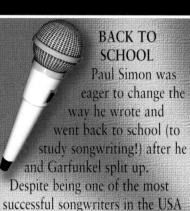

Garfunkel appeared in many films, including "Catch 22" (above).

THE GRADUATE

In 1968 Dustin Hoffman starred in the controversial film "The Graduate," the story of a college student seduced by an older woman, Mrs. Robinson. Simon and Garfunkel contributed to the soundtrack, and "Mrs. Robinson" was one of their biggest international successes.

Another successful album, "Bookends," followed and in 1969 the single "The Boxer" made the US and UK Top 10. Although the end of their working relationship was in sight, Simon and Garfunkel's biggest commercial hit yet was imminent. "Bridge Over Troubled Water" made No. 1 on both sides of the Atlantic, as did the album of the same name.

PARTING COMPANY

But Simon and Garfunkel wanted to go in different directions and in 1970 they split up. Garfunkel pursued an acting career and Simon carved his own impressive solo musical career. They did get together again – for a concert in New York in 1981 and again for a series of concerts in 1993.

BACK TO SCHOOL

Paul Simon was eager to change the way he wrote and went back to school (to study songwriting!) after he and Garfunkel split up. Despite being one of the most successful songwriters in the USA at the time, he felt he had more to learn.

He wanted to research some very different music sources, and his post-Simon and Garfunkel work certainly incorporated elements of jazz, reggae and blues.

Simon's best-selling album, "Graceland," strongly influenced by black South African music, reached No. 1 in 1986, amid accusations of exploitation from the anti-apartheid movement of South Africa.

Simon's "Graceland" tour included a large cast of South African musicians.

The SMALL FACES

For a short time during the mid '60s, a weekend ritual took place in some of the seaside resorts on the South Coast of England. "Mods" and "rockers" would meet to do battle. The mods rode motor scooters and dressed in sharp, fashionable suits with button-down collared shirts. The rockers rode motorcycles and wore studded leather outfits. Sometimes people got hurt but it was as much about parading a fashion image as fighting a rival gang.

MODS

Fashion has always been closely allied to pop music. In 1965 one group of musicians exploited their mod image with great success. Steve Marriot, aged just 18, had already released two solo singles and had stage and TV success as a child actor. He joined Ronnie Lane, Kenney Jones and Jimmy Winston and they named themselves the Small Faces. The name came from the term "faces," used for the most respected mods, and "small" because three of them were under five feet, three inches tall!

"Small Faces" May '66
"From the Beginning" May '67
"Ogdens' Nut Gone Flake"
June '68
"Small Faces Collection"
November '85

"The Singles As and Bs" June '90
"The Small Faces Boxed-
The Definitive Collection"
July '95
"The Best of the Small Faces"
July '95

FIRST HIT SINGLE

Within weeks they had met their dynamic agent, Don Arden, and released the first of their Top 20 singles on the Decca label, "Watcha Gonna Do About It?" By August 1965, organist Jimmy Winston (taller than the others) had left. Ian McLagan, an experienced organist and small in height, was the perfect replacement and the Small Faces became a household name.

Their extensive touring schedule, recording successes and TV appearances kept them in the spotlight and thousands of teenage girls pursued them. From August 1965 to July '68, they had 13 singles in the charts, most of them written by Lane and Marriot. Influenced by rhythm and blues (R&B) music, they were finding their own sound.

The first round album cover, it was designed to look like a tobacco tin.

OGDENS' NUT GONE FLAKE

The band switched to the Immediate label. In 1967 the single "Itchycoo Park" went to No. 3 in the UK charts and was their only US hit, reaching No. 16. In 1968 they released their masterpiece album, "Ogdens' Nut Gone Flake."

They took their music very seriously but were already becoming disillusioned with their pop star lifestyle. By 1969 money and management problems caused tension in the band and Marriot left to join Peter Frampton in Humble Pie.

MANAGERS' ROLE

Managers have always played a crucial role in the fortunes of bands. Talented musicians are not necessarily astute businessmen – a dynamic and knowledgeable manager can make all the difference between success and failure. Sadly, some managers took advantage of the naïveté of their artists and tied them into unfair and unlucrative contracts with the promise of greater things to follow.

There is little doubt that many bands did not reap the financial rewards their success had earned. The Small Faces felt that they had been exploited, but lengthy litigation to pursue the back payment of record royalties failed to get them anywhere.

An infamous example of a manipulative manager was Colonel Tom Parker, Elvis Presley's manager. Elvis wasn't allowed to perform outside the USA. Parker wouldn't let Elvis go alone and couldn't leave the USA himself because he was an illegal immigrant who may not have been allowed back.

Mods in uniform parkas arrive in Hastings.

THE FACES

Rod Stewart and Ron Wood joined Lane, Jones and McLagan. Called the Faces, they toured UK clubs and universities for two years and had four hit singles. Lane left to start a solo career and Wood became involved with the Rolling Stones. Stewart pursued his own solo career and in 1975 the band split up.

Four years later Jones joined the Who. McLagan, too, still works as a musician. In 1991 Marriot died in a fire at his home in Essex. Lane died in 1997 from multiple sclerosis.

A designer hired the mod band for a fashion shoot.

The SUPREMES

To succeed in the music business you need to persevere. Diane Earle and the other members of the Detroit-based vocal group the Primettes did so. They talked themselves into the offices of the Tamla Motown record label, run by Berry Gordy. Diane worked there as a part-time secretary. The group's leader, Florence (Flo) Ballard, begged Gordy to sign the girls up. He agreed, provided that they change their name. They became the Supremes, and Diane Earle was renamed Diana Ross. It was 1960.

SLOW START

None of the Supremes' early singles on Motown were hits, but Ross, Ballard, Mary Wilson and Barbara Martin worked as back-up singers. In 1962 Barbara Martin left, leaving a trio. After five flops in a row Berry Gordy was about to give up, but he decided to give them one more chance. His highly successful songwriting and production team of Holland, Dozier and Holland was asked to find something for the Supremes. In 1963 "When the Lovelight Starts

Shining Through My Eyes" entered the US Top 40. But its follow-up, "Run, Run, Run," did no better than their previous single.

Right from the start the Supremes wore glamorous matching costumes.

DIANA LEADS

Berry Gordy looked hard at the Supremes and decided that they would have more chance of success if Ross became lead singer instead of Ballard. He also realized that they needed a lot more nationwide exposure.

So they appeared on the 1964 package tour, "The Cavalcade Of Stars," for $500 per week. In 1964 the Supremes went back into the studio for their seventh attempt at recording a hit single. "Where Did Our Love Go?" was released in August.

"Meet the Supremes"
December '63

"Where Did Our Love Go?"
October '64

"Love Child"
January '69

"Compact Command Performances-
Twenty Greatest Hits"
October '86

THE HITS START

The Supremes had at last found the magic. The single went to No. 1 in the USA and No. 3 in the UK. With the support of the powerful Tamla Motown team, the Supremes were on their way. They were the first artists to have five of their singles top the US charts in succession. The talented trio toured the world.

But backstage there were tensions. Long disenchanted by Ross's hijacking of her lead singer's role, Ballard became difficult and erratic. She was asked to leave. Cindy Birdsong took over. Ballard died at the age of 32, from drug and alcohol abuse.

The hits didn't stop, and the focus was now firmly on Ross. In 1967 the Supremes became Diana Ross and the Supremes.

DIANA GOES SOLO

"Someday We'll Be Together" was the twelfth No. 1 for the trio. The Supremes kept going, but without Ross. Her very successful solo career was just beginning.

The Supremes' act was choreographed.

SOLO CAREER

When Diana Ross left the Supremes in 1970, Motown was determined that her new solo career would thrive. Her first single, "Reach Out and Touch," was written with an anti-drugs message.

Not content with her success as a singer, Ross was nominated for an Oscar for her acting debut in the film about blues singer Billie Holiday, "Lady Sings the Blues." In the late '90s, Diana Ross still tours the world, filling stadiums and concert halls with her loyal fans.

Ross sang Billie Holiday's songs in the film "Lady Sings the Blues."

The WHO

Musicians Pete Townshend, Roger Daltrey and John Entwhistle met at school in West London. In 1960, with Doug Sandom, they formed the Detours. They discovered the rhythm and blues music which was crossing the Atlantic and inspiring so many UK bands. The Detours became the Who, but not for long. Their first manager, Peter Meaden, renamed them the High Numbers and negotiated a short-lived record contract with Fontana. Keith Moon replaced Doug Sandom. Manager Peter Meaden left. The band became the Who again, with new managers, Kit Lambert and Chris Stamp.

ROCK OPERAS

Operas are dramatic stories set to music. They have been written, performed and enjoyed for centuries. All the words of the stories are sung and the stage productions today are usually lavish and colorful, using sophisticated lighting and costumes.

It is not surprising that the talented new generation of rock composers should wish to make their contribution to the genre.

Just as the works of Verdi, Mozart, Handel and Rossini have in the past, compositions produced by members of the Who, the Beatles, Pink Floyd and several other bands in the '60s and since, have brought pleasure to millions.

Maybe future generations will appreciate them just as much as the classical operas are enjoyed today, centuries after they were first written.

Daltrey played "Tommy" on stage and in the film.

MY GENERATION

By 1965 the Who was a big name around London's pubs and clubs. Playing in a low-ceilinged club, Townshend accidentally broke his guitar during an extravagant stage gesture. The crowd loved it and guitar smashing stayed in the act.

But there was much more to the Who than destroying instruments. Townshend was a gifted songwriter. His songs "I Can't Explain" and "Anyway, Anyhow, Anywhere" (which featured feedback for the first time) gave the band two Top 10 singles. Their third single became an anthem for the '60s. "My Generation," with the words "I hope I die before I get old," was a comment on the '60s pop culture – fast living, drug use and consumerism. It was their biggest hit, reaching No. 2 in the charts. Tours and TV appearances followed and the Who lived up to their image of all-imbibing party animals. Townshend's "Substitute" was another witty song about life in the fast lane and was followed by "I'm a Boy" and "Happy Jack." All three made the UK Top 5 and "Happy Jack" charted in the USA too. In 1967 the Who began the first of many US tours.

The Who were mods in 1965.

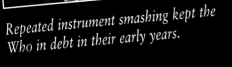

Repeated instrument smashing kept the Who in debt in their early years.

TOMMY

In 1969 Townshend's rock opera, "Tommy," was released. The powerful story of an abused deaf, dumb and blind pinball player thrust the band's career into overdrive and was later made into a film and a musical. Many hit singles and albums followed in the '70s, including another concept album, "Quadrophenia."

Sadly, in 1978, drummer Keith Moon's reveling lifestyle finally killed him.

With ex-Small Faces drummer Kenney Jones, the Who continued to record and to tour until 1982, when they split up to pursue separate careers.

"My Generation" December '65
"The Who Sell Out" January '68
"Tommy" May '69
"Live at Leeds" May '70

"Quadrophenia" November '73
"Who's Better Who's Best" March '88
"Thirty Years of Maximum R&B" January '94

STEVIE WONDER

By the time Steveland Judkins was 13 years old he had released three singles and two albums. Berry Gordy of the Tamla Motown record label renamed him Little Stevie Wonder, and when Wonder released his fourth single in August 1963 he hit the jackpot. "Fingertips" went to the top of the US charts. In the same month his live album, "The Twelve Year Old Genius," did the same. By then Little Stevie Wonder was actually 13 years and four months old.

TOURING AT TWELVE

Blind from birth, Little Stevie Wonder played the piano, harmonica, drums and bongos by the time he was eight. At ten years old he was introduced to Berry Gordy at Tamla Motown and his career began. Wonder started work in Motown's touring reviews and so had early experience of live performing.

"Fingertips" was recorded live with Wonder singing and playing harmonica against a brass background. He was the first artist ever to top the US pop singles chart, pop albums chart and ryhthm and blues (R&B) singles chart at the same time.

MARTIN LUTHER KING

Stevie Wonder was a supporter of the black rights movement in the USA which began to develop in the late '60s. Black people were campaigning for the same status and opportunities as white people. Martin Luther King, the movement's foremost leader, was murdered. Stevie Wonder campaigned to make King's birthday a national holiday.

The first Martin Luther King Day took place on January 15, 1986. At a huge concert Stevie Wonder sang "Happy Birthday," which he had written for and dedicated to his hero.

200,000 took part in the peaceful March on Washington in 1968.

"For Once in My Life"
February '69
"My Cherie Amour"
November '69
"Stevie Wonder's Greatest Hits"
August '72

"Talking Book"
January '73
"Innervisions"
August '73
"Songs in the Key of Life"
October '76

THE HITS START AND DON'T STOP

Wonder waited until 1966 for his next Top 20 entry. "Uptight (Everything's All Right)" was a song he had written himself. It reached No. 3 in the US charts, No. 14 in the UK and was massive internationally. Three hit singles followed in the same year, with seven more before the end of the decade. The biggest of them were "I Was Made to Love Her" in '67, "For Once in My Life" in '68 and "My Cherie Amour" and "Yester-Me, Yester-You, Yesterday" in 1969.

The pattern was set and Wonder continued to release hit singles year after year through the '70s and '80s. Some of his work was drawn from other sources (for example, Bob Dylan's "Blowing in the Wind" in '66) but most of the songs he wrote himself.

Wonder kept his neat collar and tie image for years.

COMING OF AGE

When Wonder reached his 21st birthday he could claim his childhood earnings. He distrusted Motown when they paid him only $1 million of an estimated $20 million earned. But he was able to renegotiate his contract. Although choosing to stay with Motown, he started his own production and publishing companies within the organization and insisted on creative freedom and an increased royalty deal. Aged just 21, his demands were met.

GENIUS

The word genius is much misused in the music business, but Stevie Wonder's enormous talent as a composer, singer and all-around musician has undeniably earned him the title he was first given as a twelve-year-old boy in Detroit.

By 1976 Wonder had a $13 million deal with Motown, the biggest in rock history.

GAZETTEER

There is no doubt that this decade produced some of the most successful and popular music of all time. Millions upon millions of records were sold all over the world. You have already read about some of the most famous '60s artists, but there were many more groups producing exciting and innovative music on both sides of the Atlantic.

The Hollies

MERSEY SOUND

After the Beatles' enormous early success, record producers realized that musical talent could be found outside London. They went to Manchester and Liverpool and signed up lots of local bands. Most of them were either talentless or one-hit wonders at best, but there were some exceptions. Close harmony groups the Hollies and the Searchers became hit recording artists. Billy J. Kramer and the Dakotas and Gerry and the Pacemakers also had long and successful careers.

The Animals

RHYTHM AND BLUES ROOTS

The blues music which had inspired the Rolling Stones did the same for several other bands which started out playing rhythm and blues (R&B). The Animals, the Yardbirds, the Pretty Things, Alan Price, Ten Years After, the Groundhogs and Manfred Mann all developed their own musical styles, but their blues roots were identical. The Yardbirds featured a guitarist who would became a household name – Eric Clapton.

Manfred Mann

PSYCHEDELIC UNDERGROUND MUSIC

Other bands played some weird but very creative music. Traffic, King Crimson, Procul Harum, Creation and the Move all caught the hippie mood of the late '60s and produced new, electronic sounds (sometimes with mystical lyrics about goblins or space travel), influenced by the psychedelic underground movement which had its roots in San Francisco.

WOMEN ARTISTS

14-year-old Millie Small reached No. 1 with "My Boy Lollipop," and Sandie Shaw, Helen Shapiro and Cilla Black all had hits. In the USA Mary Wells, Martha and the Vandellas, the Ronettes, Little Eva, the Shangri-Las and Tina Turner did the same.

Dave Clark Five

INSTRUMENTAL GROUPS

Instrumental groups became popular in the '60s. The Shadows were the most successful example in the UK, with 20 UK Top 10 hits during the decade. The Tornados' classic "Telstar" topped the US charts, an unusual achievement for a UK band at the time. The Ventures were the US equivalent of the Shadows – every guitar band in the world played their "Walk Don't Run." Johnny and the Hurricanes and the Champs introduced the saxophone (instead of the guitar) as the lead instrument in their bands with great success.

Sandie Shaw

TAMLA MOTOWN

The Detroit record company Tamla Motown produced some of the classic recordings of the decade. Smokey Robinson and the Miracles, the Temptations, Marvin Gaye, Otis Redding, Sam and Dave, the Four Tops, Percy Sledge, and many other Motown artists thrilled fans with their soulful recordings and live performances.

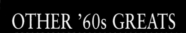
The Doors

OTHER '60s GREATS

The Byrds, the Doors and the Monkees were a big success in the UK and the USA. The Monkees were four actors in a TV series about a fictitious band. They became popular and recorded several pop songs. In the UK the quirky band the Troggs, London's Dave Clark Five, Johnny Kidd and the Pirates, Status Quo, Humble Pie and many other bands helped to make the '60s a very special decade indeed.

Marvin Gaye

The Monkees

INDEX

PHOTOGRAPHIC CREDITS Abbreviations: t-top, m-middle, b-bottom, r-right, l-left, c-center.
Front cover c & bm, 4-5, 8b, 8-9, 12b, 12-13, 14t, 14-15, 15 all, 18-19, 20-21, 21b, 22t, 28-29, 29b, 30t & b & 31tl – David Redfern / Redferns. Cover bl, 3, 9b, 18b, 23t, 25l & 29t – Redferns. Cover br, 6t, 6-7, 16t, 31m, & 31b – Michael Ochs Archive / Redferns. 5 – Bob Brunning. 6b, 16b 7 27tr – B.P / Redferns. 8t – Tommy Hanley / Redferns. 9t – Glen Baker / Redferns. 10t, 11b & 13 both – Retna. 10m, 11m & 30-31 – Corbis. 10-11, 21tl & tr & 25b – Ronald Grant Archive. 12t – Elliott Landy / Redferns. 14b, 19b, 23m & b & 28b – Hulton Getty Collection. 16-17 – Mick Hutson / Redferns. 17 – Tim Hall / Redferns. 19m – Peter Sanders / Redferns. 22-23 – Pictorial Press. 26b – Stigwood / Hemdale (courtesy Kobal). 26-27, 30m & 31tr – Cyrus Andrews / Redferns. 27tl – Richie Aaron / Redferns.